The Bi... and the Little Cat

written by Anne Giulieri
illustrated by Garry Fleming

Here is a dog.
The dog is big.

The big dog is looking at the little cat.

4

The little cat is playing.

It is playing in the grass.

The little cat can see the big dog.

The little cat looks at the tree.

The little cat goes
up, up, up the tree!

The big dog
is looking and looking.

The big dog
cannot see the little cat.

The little cat is up the tree.
It is looking at the big dog.